Multiplication

P9-DWW-267

Contents

Canadian Curriculum Press is an imprint of Telegraph Road Entertainment.

©2017 Telegraph Road Entertainment
ISBN 978-1-4876-0404-2

Author: Kevin D. Misner, B.Ed.
Senior Editor: Lisa Penttilä
Production Editor: Vin Sriniketh
Series and Cover Design: Michael P. Brodey

Selected Illustrations: Andrea Scobie and Selena Revoredo

For special bulk purchases, please contact:
sales@telegraph-rd.com

For other inquiries, please contact:
inquiries@telegraph-rd.com

We acknowledge the [financial] support of the Government of Canada

Printed in Canada

Multiplication

Dear Parents,

Learning multiplication facts takes practice. Encourage your child to spend a few minutes each day on this important skill. Frequent short sessions and repeating multiples aloud can help make newly learned facts easier to recall.

Quick recall of multiplication facts is important as children progress to higher levels of math, of course, but using multiplication to double a cookie recipe, or to find out how much money is needed to buy ten buns at the grocery store are also opportunities for children to feel proud of knowledge gained!

This workbook is a valuable tool for learning multiplication facts up to 10 x 10.

Sincerely,

Kevin D. Misner, B.Ed. and the Canadian Curriculum Press team

Terms Used in this Workbook

Factors are the numbers that are multiplied together to find a **product**. That is, factor x factor = product.

An **array** is a collection of objects arranged into equal rows or columns. Multiply the number of rows (**factor**) by the number of objects in one row (**factor**) to find the total number of objects in the array (**product**).

Skip counting by 2s, 5s, and so on teaches children the multiples of those numbers, which in turn helps them memorize multiplication facts. Encourage your child to practise skip counting by different numbers aloud each day until each pattern comes easily.

Multiplication Using Arrays

PARENTS: *Arrays can be used to visually represent multiplication.*

An **array** is a collection of objects arranged into equal rows or columns. Multiply the number of rows (**factor**) by the number of objects in one row (**factor**) to find the total number of objects in the array (**product**).

Example: The multiplication sentence for this array is

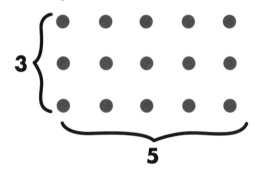

3

5

3 x 5 = 15

factor - number of rows

factor - number of dots in each row

product - total number of dots in the array

Write a multiplication sentence for each array.

_____ **x** _____ = _____

Notice: The factors here are the same as in the example above. Their different order doesn't change the product.
3 x 5 = 15 and
5 x 3 = 15

_____ **x** _____ = _____

_____ **x** _____ = _____

Multiplication Using Arrays

Using 6 dots each time, draw 4 different arrays. Answer the questions for each array.

1st array:

2 { 3 }

How many rows are there? ___2___

How many dots in each row? ___3___

How many dots altogether? ___6___

What is the multiplication sentence? ___2 x 3 = 6___

2nd array:

How many rows are there? _____

How many dots in each row? _____

How many dots altogether? _____

What is the multiplication sentence? _____

3rd array:

How many rows are there? _____

How many dots in each row? _____

How many dots altogether? _____

What is the multiplication sentence? _____

4th array:

How many rows are there? _____

How many dots in each row? _____

How many dots altogether? _____

What is the multiplication sentence? _____

Notice: Different arrays can represent one product. That means different factors can be multiplied together to make the same product.

Arrays Practice

Draw dots to create arrays for:

3 x 3	2 x 3	1 x 3	4 x 3

Can you create a math word problem that you could solve with a 3 x 3 array?

Multiplication Using Skip Counting by 2s and 3s

PARENTS:

Skip counting by 2s, 3s, and so on teaches children the multiples of those numbers, which in turn helps them memorize multiplication facts.

Skip counting can help you multiply. The example below shows 2 x 8 = 16

factor – skip by this number each time

factor – skip this number of times

product

You can use your fingers to keep track of the number of skips.

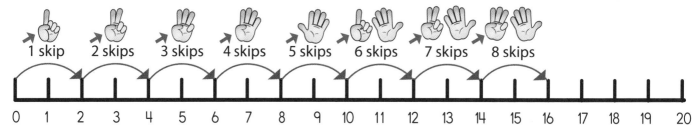

1 skip 2 skips 3 skips 4 skips 5 skips 6 skips 7 skips 8 skips

0 1 2 3 4 5 6 7 8 9 10 11 12 13 14 15 16 17 18 19 20

Skip count by 3s to find the number of lily pads in the pond. Count the number of groups. Write a multiplication sentence to match.

_____ x _____ = _____

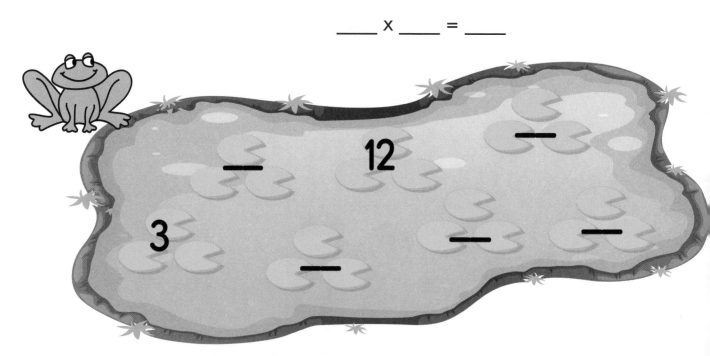

Multiplication Using Skip Counting by 5s, 10s, 4s

Skip count by 5s to find the number of balloons in all. Keep track of the number of groups with your fingers. Then write a multiplication sentence.

____ **x** ____ **=** ____

Skip count by 10s to find the number of ties on the kite tails all together. Keep track of the number of groups (kite tails) with your fingers. Then write a multiplication sentence.

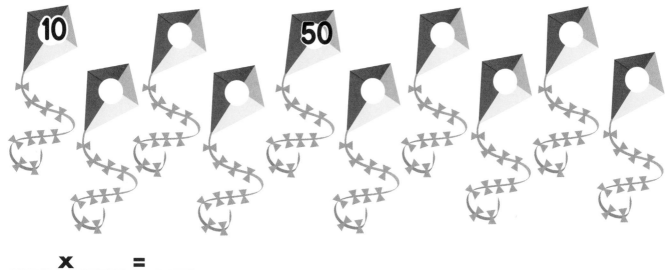

____ **x** ____ **=** ____

Skip count by 4s to find the number of leaves in all. Keep track of the number of groups with your fingers. Then write a multiplication sentence.

____ **x** ____ **=** ____

Get Ready! Get Set! Practise 1x Facts

This is an easy one!
One times any number is always the number itself!

1 x 0 = __0__   1 x 4 = ___   1 x 8 = ___

1 x 1 = __1__   1 x 5 = ___   1 x 9 = ___

1 x 2 = ___   1 x 6 = ___   1 x 10 = ___

1 x 3 = ___   1 x 7 = ___

1 x 2 = ___   1 x 1 = ___

1 x 4 = ___   1 x 3 = ___

1 x 6 = ___   1 x 5 = ___

1 x 8 = ___   1 x 7 = ___

1 x 10 = ___   1 x 9 = ___

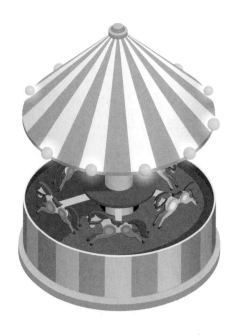

Go! Multiply to 1 x 10

1 x 0	1 x 6 **6**	1 x 5	1 x 2
1 x 7	1 x 1	1 x 3	1 x 5
1 x 2	1 x 8	1 x 7	1 x 6
1 x 9	1 x 3	1 x 8	1 x 4
1 x 4	1 x 10	1 x 9	1 x 3

Get Ready! Skip Count to Learn Multiples of 2

You can skip count using a hundred chart. Shade the multiples of 2 on the chart.

1	2	3	4	5	6	7	8	9	10
11	12	13	14	15	16	17	18	19	20
21	22	23	24	25	26	27	28	29	30
31	32	33	34	35	36	37	38	39	40
41	42	43	44	45	46	47	48	49	50
51	52	53	54	55	56	57	58	59	60
61	62	63	64	65	66	67	68	69	70
71	72	73	74	75	76	77	78	79	80
81	82	83	84	85	86	87	88	89	90
91	92	93	94	95	96	97	98	99	100

Skip count by 2s ten times. Keep track of the number of skips with the fingers. Fill the boxes with the multiples of 2. Write the matching multiplication sentence. ____x____=____

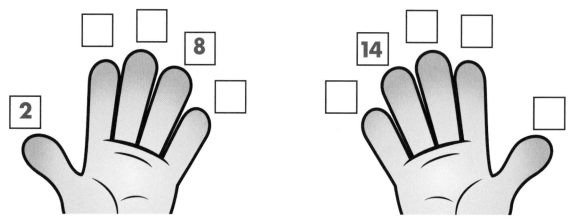

Practise skip counting aloud by 2s to 20 until you can do it without looking. Can you count higher?

Get Set! Practise 2x Facts

Fill in the blanks to skip count from 2 to 20 and back again. Then complete the multiplication sentences.

2, ___, **6**, ___, ___, ___, ___, ___, **18**, 20

20, ___, ___, ___, ___, ___, ___, **6**, ___, 2

2 x 0 = _____   2 x 4 = _____   2 x 8 = _____

2 x 1 = _____   2 x 5 = _____   2 x 9 = _____

2 x 2 = _____   2 x 6 = _____   2 x 10 = _____

2 x 3 = _____   2 x 7 = _____

    2 x 2 = _____   2 x 1 = _____

    2 x 4 = _____   2 x 3 = _____

    2 x 6 = _____   2 x 5 = _____

    2 x 8 = _____   2 x 7 = _____

    2 x 10 = _____   2 x 9 = _____

Go! Multiply to 2 x 10

2 x 6 **12**	2 x 5	2 x 4	2 x 10
2 x 1	2 x 0	2 x 2	2 x 4
2 x 8	2 x 7	2 x 5	2 x 3
2 x 3	2 x 2	2 x 6	2 x 7
2 x 10	2 x 8	2 x 9	2 x 8

Build a Mighty Memory Muscle!

After you finish this page, ask someone to read the questions aloud to you. Without looking, answer as many as you can from memory. For any you don't remember, find the answer, then repeat that multiplication sentence aloud. Memory experts say that repetition is a great way to strengthen your memory muscle and make remembering multiplication facts easy!

Get Ready! Skip Count to Learn Multiples of 3

Shade the multiples of 3 on the chart.

1	2	3	4	5	6	7	8	9	10
11	12	13	14	15	16	17	18	19	20
21	22	23	24	25	26	27	28	29	30
31	32	33	34	35	36	37	38	39	40
41	42	43	44	45	46	47	48	49	50
51	52	53	54	55	56	57	58	59	60
61	62	63	64	65	66	67	68	69	70
71	72	73	74	75	76	77	78	79	80
81	82	83	84	85	86	87	88	89	90
91	92	93	94	95	96	97	98	99	100

Skip count by 3s ten times. Keep track of the number of skips with the fingers. Fill the boxes with the multiples of 3. Write the matching multiplication sentence. ____x____=____

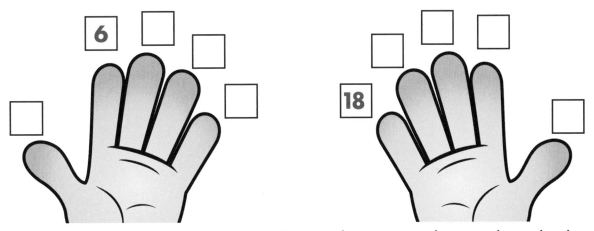

Practise skip counting aloud by 3s to 30 until you can do it without looking. Can you count higher?

Get Set! Practise 3x Facts

Fill in the blanks to skip count from 3 to 30 and back again. Then complete the multiplication sentences.

3, ___, ___, ___, **15**, ___, ___, ___, ___, 30

30, ___, **24**, ___, ___, ___, ___, ___, ___, 3

3 x 0 = ____   3 x 4 = ____   3 x 8 = ____

3 x 1 = ____   3 x 5 = ____   3 x 9 = ____

3 x 2 = ____   3 x 6 = ____   3 x 10 = ____

3 x 3 = ____   3 x 7 = ____

3 x 2 = ____   3 x 1 = ____

3 x 4 = ____   3 x 3 = ____

3 x 6 = ____   3 x 5 = ____

3 x 8 = ____   3 x 7 = ____

3 x 10 = ____   3 x 9 = ____

Go! Multiply to 3 x 10

3 x 7	3 x 10	3 x 4	3 x 3
3 x 1	3 x 0	3 x 2	3 x 5
3 x 9	3 x 8	3 x 4	3 x 6
3 x 3	3 x 2	3 x 7	3 x 9
3 x 5	3 x 10	3 x 6	3 x 8

Build a Mighty Memory Muscle!
After you finish this page, ask someone to read the questions aloud to you. Without looking, answer as many as you can from memory. For any you don't remember, find the answer, then repeat that multiplication sentence aloud. Memory experts say that repetition is a great way to strengthen your memory muscle and make remembering multiplication facts easy!

Get Ready! Skip Count to Learn Multiples of 4

Shade the multiples of 4 on the chart.

1	2	3	4	5	6	7	8	9	10
11	12	13	14	15	16	17	18	19	20
21	22	23	24	25	26	27	28	29	30
31	32	33	34	35	36	37	38	39	40
41	42	43	44	45	46	47	48	49	50
51	52	53	54	55	56	57	58	59	60
61	62	63	64	65	66	67	68	69	70
71	72	73	74	75	76	77	78	79	80
81	82	83	84	85	86	87	88	89	90
91	92	93	94	95	96	97	98	99	100

Skip count by 4s ten times. Keep track of the number of skips with the fingers. Fill the boxes with the multiples of 4. Write the matching multiplication sentence. ____x____=____

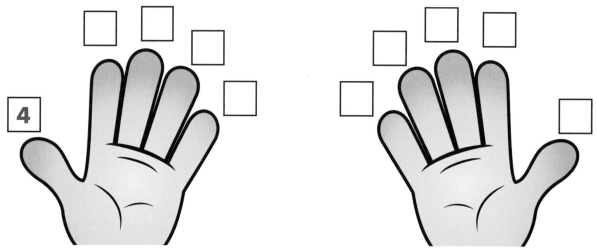

Practise skip counting aloud by 4s to 40 until you can do it without looking. Can you count higher?

Get Set! Practise 4x Facts

Fill in the blanks to skip count from 4 to 40 and back again. Then complete the multiplication sentences.

4, ___, ___, ___, ___, ___, ___, ___, ___, 40

40, ___, ___, ___, ___, **20**, ___, ___, ___, 4

$4 \times 0 =$ ____ $4 \times 4 =$ ____ $4 \times 8 =$ ____

$4 \times 1 =$ ____ $4 \times 5 =$ ____ $4 \times 9 =$ ____

$4 \times 2 =$ ____ $4 \times 6 =$ ____ $4 \times 10 =$ ____

$4 \times 3 =$ ____ $4 \times 7 =$ ____

$4 \times 2 =$ ____ $4 \times 1 =$ ____

$4 \times 4 =$ ____ $4 \times 3 =$ ____

$4 \times 6 =$ ____ $4 \times 5 =$ ____

$4 \times 8 =$ ____ $4 \times 7 =$ ____

$4 \times 10 =$ ____ $4 \times 9 =$ ____

Go! Multiply to 4 x 10

4 x 6	4 x 0	4 x 4	4 x 3
4 x 1	4 x 7	4 x 9	4 x 5
4 x 7	4 x 6	4 x 8	4 x 10
4 x 4	4 x 10	4 x 3	4 x 9
4 x 8	4 x 2	4 x 5	4 x 2

Build a Mighty Memory Muscle!

After you finish this page, ask someone to read the questions aloud to you. Without looking, answer as many as you can from memory. For any you don't remember, find the answer, then repeat that multiplication sentence aloud. Memory experts say that repetition is a great way to strengthen your memory muscle and make remembering multiplication facts easy!

Learn the 4x Double-Double Trick

Here is a trick to multiply any number by 4. Just double the number that is to be multiplied by 4, and then double it again. (Remember: **Double** is another way to say **multiply by 2**.)

Example: 4 x 5 = ?

First, double the 5 to get 10.

Then, double the 10 to get 20.

So, 4 x 5 = 20

Try the **double-double** trick on the questions below.

4	4	4	4
x 6	x 10	x 3	x 2

4	4	4	4
x 4	x 7	x 9	x 8

Use the 4x double-double trick to check your answers on page 18.

One More Lap! Review 1x, 2x, 3x, 4x Facts

2 x 2 =_____   4 x 9 =_____   1 x 7 =_____

4 x 6 =_____   3 x 8 =_____   3 x 3 =_____

3 x 7 =_____   4 x 10 =_____   2 x 8 =_____

2 x 10 =_____   2 x 7 =_____   2 x 6 =_____

1 x 5 =_____   3 x 6 =_____   4 x 7 =_____

4 x 3 =_____   4 x 2 =_____   3 x 4 =_____

3 x 5 =_____   2 x 3 =_____   1 x 10 =_____

4 x 4 =_____   2 x 5 =_____   2 x 9 =_____

3 x 9 =_____   3 x 2 =_____   4 x 8 =_____

2 x 4 =_____   4 x 5 =_____   3 x 10 =_____

Get Ready! Skip Count to Learn Multiples of 5

Shade the multiples of 5 on the chart.

1	2	3	4	5	6	7	8	9	10
11	12	13	14	15	16	17	18	19	20
21	22	23	24	25	26	27	28	29	30
31	32	33	34	35	36	37	38	39	40
41	42	43	44	45	46	47	48	49	50
51	52	53	54	55	56	57	58	59	60
61	62	63	64	65	66	67	68	69	70
71	72	73	74	75	76	77	78	79	80
81	82	83	84	85	86	87	88	89	90
91	92	93	94	95	96	97	98	99	100

Skip count by 5s ten times. Keep track of the number of skips with the fingers. Fill the boxes with the multiples of 5. Write the matching multiplication sentence. ____x____=____

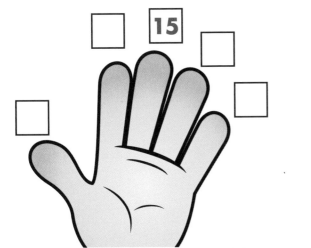
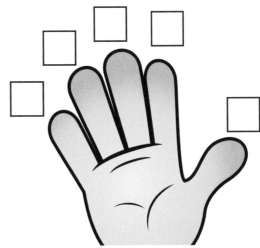

Practise skip counting aloud by 5s to 50 until you can do it without looking. Can you count higher?

Get Set! Practise 5x Facts

Fill in the blanks to skip count from 5 to 50 and back again. Then complete the multiplication sentences.

5, ___, ___, ___, ___, ___, ___, ___, ___, 50

50, ___, ___, ___, ___, ___, ___, ___, ___, 5

$5 \times 0 =$ ____ $5 \times 4 =$ ____ $5 \times 8 =$ ____

$5 \times 1 =$ ____ $5 \times 5 =$ ____ $5 \times 9 =$ ____

$5 \times 2 =$ ____ $5 \times 6 =$ ____ $5 \times 10 =$ ____

$5 \times 3 =$ ____ $5 \times 7 =$ ____

$5 \times 2 =$ ____ $5 \times 1 =$ ____

$5 \times 4 =$ ____ $5 \times 3 =$ ____

$5 \times 6 =$ ____ $5 \times 5 =$ ____

$5 \times 8 =$ ____ $5 \times 7 =$ ____

$5 \times 10 =$ ____ $5 \times 9 =$ ____

Go! Multiply to 5 x 10

5 x 9	5 x 6	5 x 10	5 x 3
5 x 1	5 x 7	5 x 6	5 x 5
5 x 8	5 x 9	5 x 8	5 x 7
5 x 3	5 x 10	5 x 4	5 x 0
5 x 5	5 x 2	5 x 4	5 x 2

Get Ready! Skip Count to Learn Multiples of 6

Shade the multiples of 6 on the chart.

1	2	3	4	5	6	7	8	9	10
11	12	13	14	15	16	17	18	19	20
21	22	23	24	25	26	27	28	29	30
31	32	33	34	35	36	37	38	39	40
41	42	43	44	45	46	47	48	49	50
51	52	53	54	55	56	57	58	59	60
61	62	63	64	65	66	67	68	69	70
71	72	73	74	75	76	77	78	79	80
81	82	83	84	85	86	87	88	89	90
91	92	93	94	95	96	97	98	99	100

Skip count by 6s ten times. Keep track of the number of skips with the fingers. Fill the boxes with the multiples of 6. Write the matching multiplication sentence. ____x____=____

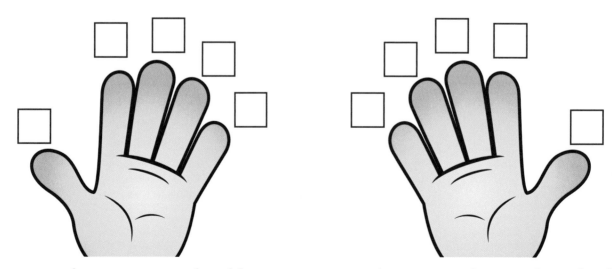

Practise skip counting aloud by 6s to 60 until you can do it without looking at the chart. Can you count higher?

Get Set! Practise 6x Facts

Fill in the blanks to skip count from 6 to 60 and back again. Then complete the multiplication sentences.

6, ___, ___, ___, ___, ___, ___, ___, ___, 60

60, ___, ___, ___, ___, ___, ___, ___, ___, 6

6 x 0 = ____   6 x 4 = ____   6 x 8 = ____

6 x 1 = ____   6 x 5 = ____   6 x 9 = ____

6 x 2 = ____   6 x 6 = ____   6 x 10 = ____

6 x 3 = ____   6 x 7 = ____

6 x 2 = ____   6 x 1 = ____

6 x 4 = ____   6 x 3 = ____

6 x 6 = ____   6 x 5 = ____

6 x 8 = ____   6 x 7 = ____

6 x 10 = ____   6 x 9 = ____

Go! Multiply to 6 x 10

6 x 1	6 x 3	6 x 4	6 x 7
6 x 3	6 x 8	6 x 6	6 x 5
6 x 7	6 x 9	6 x 8	6 x 10
6 x 5	6 x 10	6 x 4	6 x 9
6 x 2	6 x 6	6 x 2	6 x 0

Get Ready! Skip Count to Learn Multiples of 7

Shade the multiples of 7 on the chart.

1	2	3	4	5	6	7	8	9	10
11	12	13	14	15	16	17	18	19	20
21	22	23	24	25	26	27	28	29	30
31	32	33	34	35	36	37	38	39	40
41	42	43	44	45	46	47	48	49	50
51	52	53	54	55	56	57	58	59	60
61	62	63	64	65	66	67	68	69	70
71	72	73	74	75	76	77	78	79	80
81	82	83	84	85	86	87	88	89	90
91	92	93	94	95	96	97	98	99	100

Skip count by 7s ten times. Keep track of the number of skips with the fingers. Fill the boxes with the multiples of 7. Write the matching multiplication sentence. ____x____=____

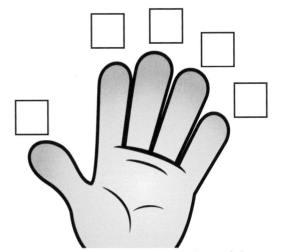
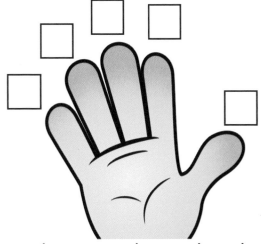

Practise skip counting aloud by 7s to 70 until you can do it without looking at the chart. Can you count higher?

Get Set! Practise 7x Facts

Fill in the blanks to skip count from 7 to 70 and back again. Then complete the multiplication sentences.

7, ___, ___, ___, ___, ___, ___, ___, ___, 70

70, ___, ___, ___, ___, ___, ___, ___, ___, 7

7 x 0 = ____   7 x 4 = ____   7 x 8 = ____

7 x 1 = ____   7 x 5 = ____   7 x 9 = ____

7 x 2 = ____   7 x 6 = ____   7 x 10 = ____

7 x 3 = ____   7 x 7 = ____

7 x 2 = ____   7 x 1 = ____

7 x 4 = ____   7 x 3 = ____

7 x 6 = ____   7 x 5 = ____

7 x 8 = ____   7 x 7 = ____

7 x 10 = ____   7 x 9 = ____

Go! Multiply to 7 x 10

7 x 5	7 x 6	7 x 3	7 x 10
7 x 1	7 x 7	7 x 2	7 x 8
7 x 3	7 x 4	7 x 7	7 x 4
7 x 8	7 x 2	7 x 6	7 x 9
7 x 5	7 x 10	7 x 9	7 x 4

One More Lap! Review 5x, 6x, 7x Facts

5 x 2 = ____	5 x 7 = ____	5 x 8 = ____
6 x 9 = ____	6 x 6 = ____	6 x 4 = ____
7 x 6 = ____	5 x 9 = ____	5 x 6 = ____
6 x 7 = ____	6 x 2 = ____	7 x 7 = ____
5 x 10 = ____	5 x 3 = ____	6 x 4 = ____
7 x 3 = ____	7 x 8 = ____	5 x 9 = ____
6 x 5 = ____	5 x 5 = ____	5 x 8 = ____
7 x 4 = ____	6 x 2 = ____	6 x 10 = ____
6 x 9 = ____	5 x 10 = ____	7 x 0 = ____
6 x 8 = ____	7 x 5 = ____	6 x 1 = ____
7 x 10 = ____	5 x 3 = ____	5 x 0 = ____

Let's Go Around Again!
Review 1x, 2x, 3x, 4x, 5x, 6x, 7x Facts

2 x 2 = ____	7 x 7 = ____	3 x 6 = ____	3 x 3 = ____
5 x 2 = ____	3 x 9 = ____	7 x 3 = ____	2 x 8 = ____
4 x 6 = ____	6 x 9 = ____	2 x 9 = ____	2 x 6 = ___
5 x 3 = ____	7 x 6 = ____	7 x 4= ____	1 x 1 = ____
3 x 7 = ____	7 x 9 = ____	4 x 2 = ____	7 x 7 = ____
5 x 6 = ____	2 x 4 = ____	5 x 9 = ____	4 x 7 = ____
2 x 10 = ____	5 x 5 = ____	2 x 3 = ____	3 x 4 = ____
4 x 3 = ____	4 x 9 = ____	6 x 2 = ____	5 x 8 = ____
5 x 4 = ____	6 x 4 = ____	6 x 8 = ____	2 x 9 = ____
3 x 5 = ____	3 x 8 = ____	2 x 5 = ____	1 x 3= ____
1 x 10 = ____	4 x10 = ____	5 x 10 = ____	6 x 10 = ____
6 x 6 = ____	6 x 5 = ____	3 x 2 = ____	4 x 8 = ____
5 x 3 = ____	2 x 7 = ____	7 x 10 = ____	7 x 5 = ____
7 x 4 = ____	5 x 8 = ____	4 x 5 = ____	3 x 10 = ____
4 x 4 = ____	2 x 3 = ____	7 x 3 = ____	6 x 2 = ____

Get Ready! Skip Count to Learn Multiples of 8

Shade the multiples of 8 on the chart.

1	2	3	4	5	6	7	8	9	10
11	12	13	14	15	16	17	18	19	20
21	22	23	24	25	26	27	28	29	30
31	32	33	34	35	36	37	38	39	40
41	42	43	44	45	46	47	48	49	50
51	52	53	54	55	56	57	58	59	60
61	62	63	64	65	66	67	68	69	70
71	72	73	74	75	76	77	78	79	80
81	82	83	84	85	86	87	88	89	90
91	92	93	94	95	96	97	98	99	100

Skip count by 8s ten times. Keep track of the number of skips with the fingers. Fill the boxes with the multiples of 8. Write the matching multiplication sentence. _____ x _____ = _____

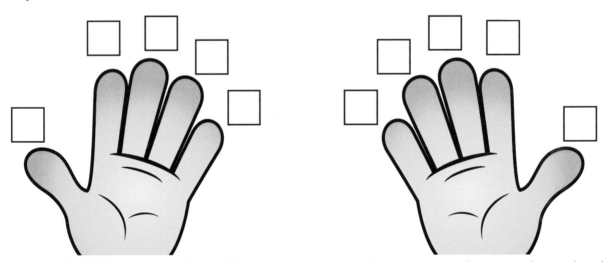

Practise skip counting aloud by 8s to 80 until you can do it without looking. Can you count higher?

Get Set! Practise 8x Facts

Fill in the blanks to skip count from 8 to 80 and back to 8. Then complete the multiplication sentences.

8, ___, ___, ___, ___, ___, ___, ___, ___, 80

80, ___, ___, ___, ___, ___, ___, ___, ___, 8

8 x 0 = ____   8 x 4 = ____   8 x 8 = ____

8 x 1 = ____   8 x 5 = ____   8 x 9 = ____

8 x 2 = ____   8 x 6 = ____   8 x 10 = ____

8 x 3 = ____   8 x 7 = ____

8 x 2 = ____   8 x 1 = ____

8 x 4 = ____   8 x 3 = ____

8 x 6 = ____   8 x 5 = ____

8 x 8 = ____   8 x 7 = ____

8 x 10 = ____   8 x 9 = ____

Go! Multiply to 8 x 10

8 x 5	8 x 2	8 x 10	8 x 6
8 x 1	8 x 6	8 x 5	8 x 3
8 x 9	8 x 7	8 x 4	8 x 9
8 x 3	8 x 8	8 x 0	8 x 7
8 x 7	8 x 9	8 x 10	8 x 2

Get Ready! Skip Count to Learn Multiples of 9

Shade the multiples of 9 on the chart.

1	2	3	4	5	6	7	8	9	10
11	12	13	14	15	16	17	18	19	20
21	22	23	24	25	26	27	28	29	30
31	32	33	34	35	36	37	38	39	40
41	42	43	44	45	46	47	48	49	50
51	52	53	54	55	56	57	58	59	60
61	62	63	64	65	66	67	68	69	70
71	72	73	74	75	76	77	78	79	80
81	82	83	84	85	86	87	88	89	90
91	92	93	94	95	96	97	98	99	100

Skip count by 9s ten times. Keep track of the number of skips with the fingers. Fill the boxes with the multiples of 9. Write the matching multiplication sentence. ____x____=____

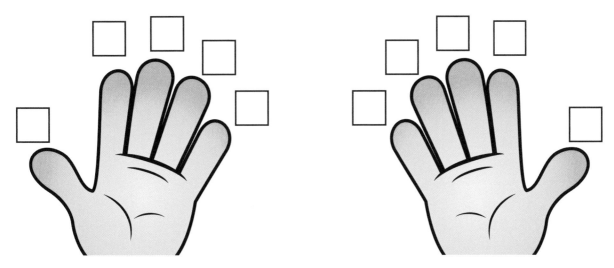

Practise skip counting aloud by 9s to 90 until you can do it without looking. Can you count higher?

Get Set! Practise 9x Facts

Fill in the blanks to skip count from 9 to 90 and back to 9. Then complete the multiplication sentences.

9, ___, ___, ___, ___, ___, ___, ___, ___, 90

90, ___, ___, ___, ___, ___, ___, ___, ___, 9

9 x 0 = ____   9 x 4 = ____   9 x 8 = ____

9 x 1 = ____   9 x 5 = ____   9 x 9 = ____

9 x 2 = ____   9 x 6 = ____   9 x 10 = ____

9 x 3 = ____   9 x 7 = ____

9 x 2 = ____   9 x 1 = ____

9 x 4 = ____   9 x 3 = ____

9 x 6 = ____   9 x 5 = ____

9 x 8 = ____   9 x 7 = ____

9 x 10 = ____   9 x 9 = ____

Go! Multiply to 9 x 10

9
x 1
___

9
x 7
___

9
x 4
___

9
x 6
___

9
x 6
___

9
x 8
___

9
x 7
___

9
x 9
___

9
x 3
___

9
x 6
___

9
x 4
___

9
x 5
___

9
x 8
___

9
x 10
___

9
x 7
___

9
x 0
___

9
x 5
___

9
x 2
___

9
x 3
___

9
x 9
___

Learn the Handy 9x Trick

Multiply any number from 1 to 9 by nine using this trick. Let's say you wanted to multiply 9 x 7.

Step 1 | Hold up all 10 of your fingers.
Imagine they are numbered 1 through 10.

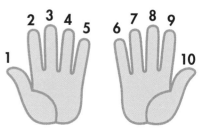

Step 2 | Since you're multiplying 9 x 7, fold down the 7th finger.

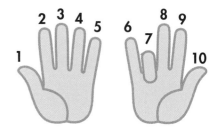

Step 3 | Each finger to the left of the folded finger represents 10.

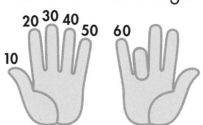

6 x 10

Add the 10s to the left of the folded finger. In this example, the 10s add up to (60.)

Step 4 | Each finger to the right of the folded finger represents 1.

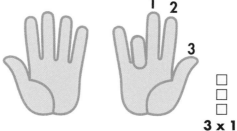

3 x 1

Add the 1s to the right of the folded finger. In this example, there are (3.)

Step 5 | Add up your fingers and the total is the answer.
(60) + (3) = 63. So the answer: 9 x 7 = 63.

Learn the Handy 9x Trick

Remember: Whatever number you want to multiply by 9, that's the finger you fold down.

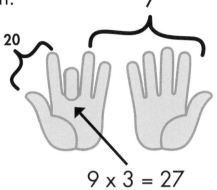

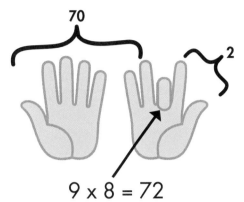

9 x 3 = 27   9 x 8 = 72

Tell which multiplication fact is shown by the fingers in these pictures. Write the multiplication sentence.

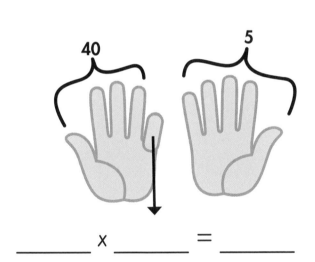

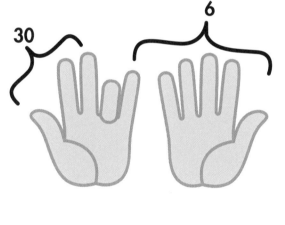

_____ x _____ = _____   _____ x _____ = _____

Use your new trick to solve these.

9 x 2 = ⬚   9 x 8 = ⬚

9 x 4 = ⬚   9 x 9 = ⬚

9 x 6 = ⬚   9 x 7 = ⬚

Use this trick to check your answers on page 37.

Get Ready! Skip Count to Learn Multiples of 10

Shade the multiples of 10 on the chart.

1	2	3	4	5	6	7	8	9	10
11	12	13	14	15	16	17	18	19	20
21	22	23	24	25	26	27	28	29	30
31	32	33	34	35	36	37	38	39	40
41	42	43	44	45	46	47	48	49	50
51	52	53	54	55	56	57	58	59	60
61	62	63	64	65	66	67	68	69	70
71	72	73	74	75	76	77	78	79	80
81	82	83	84	85	86	87	88	89	90
91	92	93	94	95	96	97	98	99	100

Skip count by 10s ten times. Keep track of the number of skips with the fingers. Fill the boxes with the multiples of 10. Write the matching multiplication sentence. ____x____=____

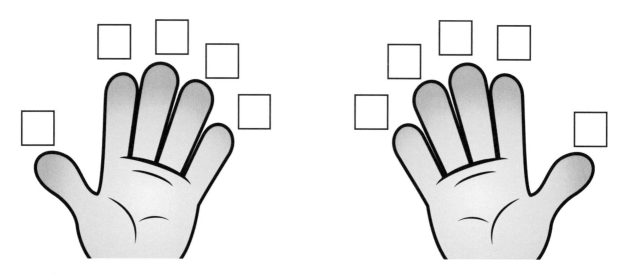

Practise skip counting aloud by 10s to 100 until you can do it without looking. Can you count higher?

Get Set! Practise 10x Facts

Fill in the blanks to skip count from 10 to 100 and back to 10. Then complete the multiplication sentences.

10, ___, ___, ___, ___, ___, ___, ___, ___, 100

100, ___, ___, ___, ___, ___, ___, ___, ___, 10

10 x 0 = ____   10 x 4 = ____   10 x 8 = ____

10 x 1 = ____   10 x 5 = ____   10 x 9 = ____

10 x 2 = ____   10 x 6 = ____   10 x 10 = ____

10 x 3 = ____   10 x 7 = ____

10 x 2 = ____   10 x 1 = ____

10 x 4 = ____   10 x 3 = ____

10 x 6 = ____   10 x 5 = ____

10 x 8 = ____   10 x 7 = ____

10 x 10 = ____   10 x 9 = ____

Go! Multiply to 10 x 10

10 x 0	10 x 6	10 x 1	10 x 3
10 x 10	10 x 3	10 x 9	10 x 5
10 x 2	10 x 9	10 x 2	10 x 8
10 x 7	10 x 8	10 x 6	10 x 7
10 x 4	10 x 10	10 x 5	10 x 4
10 x 8	10 x 9	10 x 4	10 x 10

One More Lap! Review 8x, 9x, 10x Facts

8 x 2 = _____   9 x 8 = _____   9 x 3 = _____

10 x 6 = _____   10 x 10 = _____   8 x 8 = _____

9 x 7 = _____   8 x 3 = _____   8 x 6 = _____

8 x 10 = _____   8 x 7 = _____   10 x 7 = _____

10 x 3 = _____   9 x 6 = _____   9 x 4 = _____

9 x 5 = _____   8 x 2 = _____   8 x 9 = _____

10 x 4 = _____   10 x 2 = _____   10 x 8 = _____

9 x 9 = _____   8 x 3 = _____   9 x 10 = _____

8 x 4 = _____   8 x 5 = _____   8 x 1 = _____

10 x 9 = _____   9 x 2 = _____   10 x 5 = _____

You're Off and Running! Review 1x, 2x, 3x, 4x, 5x, 6x, 7x, 8x, 9x, 10x Facts

9 x 10 =____   3 x 7 =____   3 x 5 =____   4 x 4 =____

1 x 2 =____   9 x 3 =____   8 x 7 =____   9 x 7 =____

10 x 8 =____   5 x 6 =____   7 x 1 =____   7 x 7 =____

5 x 2 =____   10 x 5 =____   10 x 10 =____   8 x 2 =____

8 x 9 =____   2 x 10 =____   9 x 8 =____   3 x 9 =____

9 x 4 =____   9 x 2 =____   6 x 6 =____   6 x 9 =____

10 x 7 =____   8 x 5 =____   8 x 4 =____   7 x 6 =____

4 x 6 =____   4 x 3 =____   5 x 3 =____   7 x 9 =____

8 x 6 =____   8 x 5 =____   9 x 9 =____   2 x 4 =____

5 x 3 =____   5 x 4 =____   7 x 4 =____   6 x 6 =____

8 x 8 =____   9 x 6 =____   9 x 5 =____

You're Off and Running! Review 1x, 2x, 3x, 4x, 5x, 6x, 7x, 8x, 9x, 10x Facts

5 x 5	7 x 3	3 x 2	2 x 9
4 x 9	7 x 4	7 x 10	6 x 10
6 x 4	4 x 2	4 x 5	4 x 8
3 x 8	5 x 9	3 x 3	7 x 5
4 x 10	2 x 3	2 x 8	3 x 10
6 x 5	6 x 2	2 x 6	6 x 2
2 x 7	6 x 8	4 x 7	7 x 3
5 x 8	2 x 5	3 x 4	1 x 6
3 x 6	5 x 10	5 x 8	10 x 10

Find the Missing Number

For 2 players. Cut out the red and blue markers or use small coins to play. Players take turns covering three numbers, one from each section, to make a multiplication sentence. When both players make no mistakes in 10 turns each, everyone wins! An example is highlighted in red.

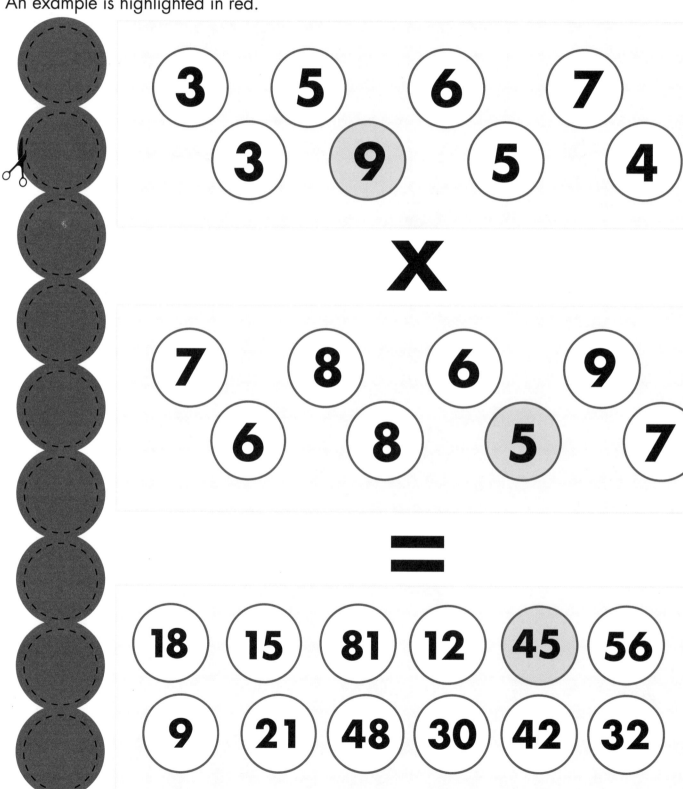

$$4 \quad 8 \quad 4 \quad 6$$

$$8 \quad 3 \quad 3 \quad 5$$

X

$$5 \quad 3 \quad 6 \quad 3$$

$$6 \quad 9 \quad 9 \quad 5$$

=

$$64 \quad 40 \quad 24 \quad 72 \quad 54 \quad 36$$

$$63 \quad 20 \quad 25 \quad 27 \quad 28 \quad 35$$

Find the Missing Numbers

Multiply the factor in the centre orange circle by each factor in the blue ring to get the product in the outer yellow ring. Fill in the missing factors and products.

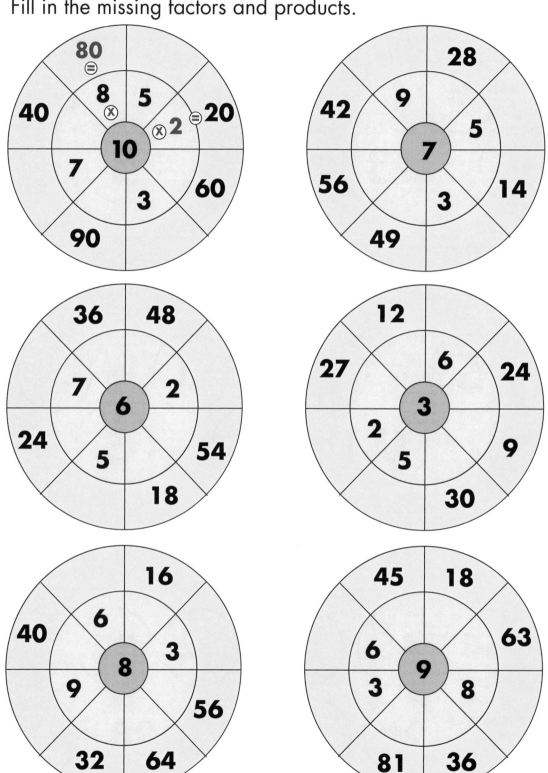

Dice Toss Multiplication Game

Roll a pair of dice. Fill in the first two bubbles with the numbers on each die. Then complete the multiplication sentence.

Example: ④ x ② = ⑧

◯ X ◯ = ◯   ◯ X ◯ = ◯

◯ X ◯ = ◯   ◯ X ◯ = ◯

◯ X ◯ = ◯   ◯ X ◯ = ◯

◯ X ◯ = ◯   ◯ X ◯ = ◯

◯ X ◯ = ◯   ◯ X ◯ = ◯

◯ X ◯ = ◯   ◯ X ◯ = ◯

◯ X ◯ = ◯   ◯ X ◯ = ◯

Multiplication Tic-Tac-Toe

Play like normal tic-tac-toe, but each player must correctly answer a multiplication fact before getting a square.

9 x 7	5 x 7	3 x 9
2 x 9	6 x 9	8 x 8
10 x 7	7 x 8	6 x 6

10 x 8	7 x 7	6 x 5
4 x 7	6 x 8	8 x 9
9 x 2	3 x 7	3 x 6

2 x 4	4 x 6	9 x 4
2 x 7	3 x 4	9 x 6
8 x 7	9 x 9	10 x 6

10 x 2	6 x 7	4 x 6
2 x 6	9 x 8	8 x 3
4 x 9	5 x 3	6 x 6

6 x 5	8 x 10	8 x 4
2 x 3	3 x 8	5 x 5
9 x 5	6 x 3	7 x 9

4 x 9	8 x 6	8 x 7
5 x 8	7 x 9	7 x 6
8 x 5	3 x 2	4 x 9

Solve the Riddle

Solve the multiplication fact and print the letter in the box above the right answer.

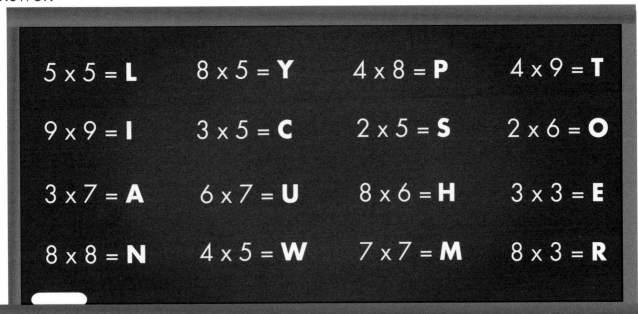

5 x 5 = **L**	8 x 5 = **Y**	4 x 8 = **P**	4 x 9 = **T**
9 x 9 = **I**	3 x 5 = **C**	2 x 5 = **S**	2 x 6 = **O**
3 x 7 = **A**	6 x 7 = **U**	8 x 6 = **H**	3 x 3 = **E**
8 x 8 = **N**	4 x 5 = **W**	7 x 7 = **M**	8 x 3 = **R**

Can you figure out the riddle?

49	42	25	36	81	32	25	81	15	21	36	81	12	64

81	10

9	21	10	40

20	81	36	48

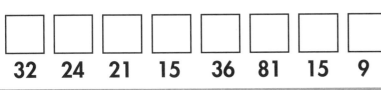

32	24	21	15	36	81	15	9

Missing Factors Fill Up

Fill in the missing factors in the boxes:

9 x ☐ = 27   5 x ☐ = 20   3 x ☐ = 24   2 x ☐ = 16

7 x ☐ = 49   8 x ☐ = 40   6 x ☐ = 36   5 x ☐ = 35

4 x ☐ = 40   7 x ☐ = 56   3 x ☐ = 18   4 x ☐ = 24

3 x ☐ = 27   8 x ☐ = 64   6 x ☐ = 48   2 x ☐ = 18

7 x ☐ = 63   5 x ☐ = 10   3 x ☐ = 21   4 x ☐ = 28

9 x ☐ = 45   6 x ☐ = 30   4 x ☐ = 12   1 x ☐ = 8

Multiplication Chart Practice

Multiply each factor in the left column by each factor in the top row. Fill in the missing products where the rows and columns meet.

Example: 2 x 2 = 4

X	1	2	3	4	5	6	7	8	9	10
1			3				7		9	
2		4				12				20
3			9				21		27	
4				16				32		40
5				20			35		45	
6			18					48		
7		14			35					70
8			24				56			80
9				36					81	
10		20			50			80		

Multiplication Chart Practice

Fill in the 2s, 5s and 10s rows and columns.

x	1	2	3	4	5	6	7	8	9	10
1		2			5					10
2	2	4			10					20
3										
4										
5	5	10								
6										
7										
8										
9										
10	10	20								

2, ——, ——, ——, ——, ——, ——, ——, ——, ——.
+2   +2   +2   +2   +2   +2   +2   +2   +2

5, ——, ——, ——, ——, ——, ——, ——, ——, ——.
+5   +5   +5   +5

10, ——, ——, ——, ——, ——, ——, ——, ——, ——.
+10 +10 +10 +10

Multiplication Chart Practice
Fill in the 3s, 6s and 9s rows and columns.

x	1	2	3	4	5	6	7	8	9	10
1										
2										
3										
4										
5										
6										
7										
8										
9										
10										

   +3   +3   +3   +3   +3   +3   +3   +3   +3

3, ——, ——, ——, ——, ——, ——, ——, ——, ——.

   +6   +6   +6   +6

6, ——, ——, ——, ——, ——, ——, ——, ——, ——.

   +9   +9   +9   +9

9, ——, ——, ——, ——, ——, ——, ——, ——, ——.

Multiplication Chart Practice

Fill in the 1s and 7s rows and columns.

X	1	2	3	4	5	6	7	8	9	10
1										
2										
3										
4										
5										
6										
7										
8										
9										
10										

1, +1 ___, +1 ___, +1 ___, +1 ___, +1 ___, +1 ___, +1 ___, +1 ___, +1 ___.

7, +7 ___, +7 ___, +7 ___, +7 ___, ___, ___, ___, ___, ___.

Multiplication Chart Practice

Fill in the 4s and 8s rows and columns.

x	1	2	3	4	5	6	7	8	9	10
1										
2										
3										
4										
5										
6										
7										
8										
9										
10										

+4   +4   +4   +4   +4   +4   +4   +4   +4

4, ___, ___, ___, ___, ___, ___, ___, ___, ___.

+8   +8   +8   +8

8, ___, ___, ___, ___, ___, ___, ___, ___, ___.

Multiplication Facts 1x1 to 10x10

1x1=1	3x1=3	5x1=5	7x1=7	9x1=9
1x2=2	3x2=6	5x2=10	7x2=14	9x2=18
1x3=3	3x3=9	5x3=15	7x3=21	9x3=27
1x4=4	3x4=12	5x4=20	7x4=28	9x4=36
1x5=5	3x5=15	5x5=25	7x5=35	9x5=45
1x6=6	3x6=18	5x6=30	7x6=42	9x6=54
1x7=7	3x7=21	5x7=35	7x7=49	9x7=63
1x8=8	3x8=24	5x8=40	7x8=56	9x8=72
1x9=9	3x9=27	5x9=45	7x9=63	9x9=81
1x10=10	3x10=30	5x10=50	7x10=70	9x10=90

2x1=2	4x1=4	6x1=6	8x1=8	10x1=10
2x2=4	4x2=8	6x2=12	8x2=16	10x2=20
2x3=6	4x3=12	6x3=18	8x3=24	10x3=30
2x4=8	4x4=16	6x4=24	8x4=32	10x4=40
2x5=10	4x5=20	6x5=30	8x5=40	10x5=50
2x6=12	4x6=24	6x6=36	8x6=48	10x6=60
2x7=14	4x7=28	6x7=42	8x7=56	10x7=70
2x8=16	4x8=32	6x8=48	8x8=64	10x8=80
2x9=18	4x9=36	6x9=54	8x9=72	10x9=90
2x10=20	4x10=40	6x10=60	8x10=80	10x10=100

Page 3

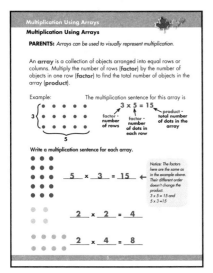

Multiplication Using Arrays

PARENTS: *Arrays can be used to visually represent multiplication.*

An **array** is a collection of objects arranged into equal rows or columns. Multiply the number of rows (**factor**) by the number of objects in one row (**factor**) to find the total number of objects in the array (**product**).

The multiplication sentence for this array is

$$3 \times 5 = 15$$

Write a multiplication sentence for each array.

$$5 \times 3 = 15$$
$$2 \times 2 = 4$$
$$2 \times 4 = 8$$

Page 4

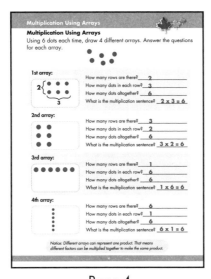

Multiplication Using Arrays

Using 6 dots each time, draw 4 different arrays. Answer the questions for each array.

1st array:
How many rows are there? 2
How many dots in each row? 3
How many dots altogether? 6
What is the multiplication sentence? 2 x 3 = 6

2nd array:
How many rows are there? 3
How many dots in each row? 2
How many dots altogether? 6
What is the multiplication sentence? 3 x 2 = 6

3rd array:
How many rows are there? 1
How many dots in each row? 6
How many dots altogether? 6
What is the multiplication sentence? 1 x 6 = 6

4th array:
How many rows are there? 6
How many dots in each row? 1
How many dots altogether? 6
What is the multiplication sentence? 6 x 1 = 6

Page 5

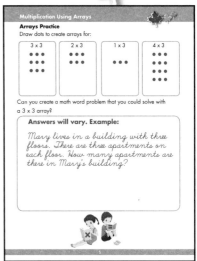

Arrays Practice

Draw dots to create arrays for:

3 x 3   2 x 3   1 x 3   4 x 3

Can you create a math word problem that you could solve with a 3 x 3 array?

Answers will vary. Example:

Mary lives in a building with three floors. There are three apartments on each floor. How many apartments are there in Mary's building?

Page 6

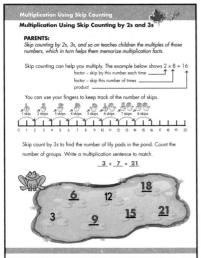

Multiplication Using Skip Counting by 2s and 3s

PARENTS: *Skip counting by 2s, 3s, and so on teaches children the multiples of those numbers, which in turn helps them memorize multiplication facts.*

Skip count by 3s to find the number of lily pads in the pond. Count the number of groups. Write a multiplication sentence to match.

$$3 \times 7 = 21$$

Page 7

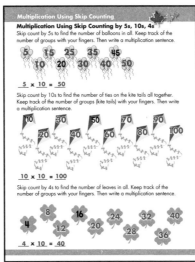

Multiplication Using Skip Counting by 5s, 10s, 4s

Skip count by 5s to find the number of balloons in all. Keep track of the number of groups with your fingers. Then write a multiplication sentence.

$$5 \times 10 = 50$$

$$10 \times 10 = 100$$

$$4 \times 10 = 40$$

Page 8

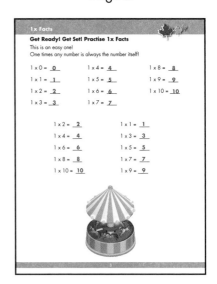

Get Ready! Get Set! Practise 1x Facts

This is an easy one!
One times any number is always the number itself!

1 x 0 = 0   1 x 4 = 4   1 x 8 = 8
1 x 1 = 1   1 x 5 = 5   1 x 9 = 9
1 x 2 = 2   1 x 6 = 6   1 x 10 = 10
1 x 3 = 3   1 x 7 = 7

1 x 2 = 2   1 x 1 = 1
1 x 4 = 4   1 x 3 = 3
1 x 6 = 6   1 x 5 = 5
1 x 8 = 8   1 x 7 = 7
1 x 10 = 10   1 x 9 = 9

Page 9

Go! Multiply to 1 x 10

Page 10

Get Ready! Skip Count to Learn Multiples of 2

You can skip count using a hundred chart. Shade the multiples of 2 on the chart.

Skip count by 2s ten times. Keep track of the number of skips with the fingers. Fill the boxes with the multiples of 2. Write the matching multiplication sentence. 2 x 10 = 20

Page 11

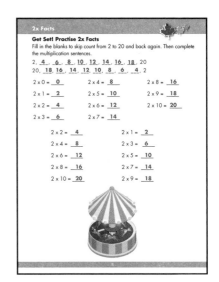

Get Set! Practise 2x Facts

Fill in the blanks to skip count from 2 to 20 and back again. Then complete the multiplication sentences.

2, 4, 6, 8, 10, 12, 14, 16, 18, 20
20, 18, 16, 14, 12, 10, 8, 6, 4, 2

2 x 0 = 0   2 x 4 = 8   2 x 8 = 16
2 x 1 = 2   2 x 5 = 10   2 x 9 = 18
2 x 2 = 4   2 x 6 = 12   2 x 10 = 20
2 x 3 = 6   2 x 7 = 14

2 x 2 = 4   2 x 1 = 2
2 x 4 = 8   2 x 3 = 6
2 x 6 = 12   2 x 5 = 10
2 x 8 = 16   2 x 7 = 14
2 x 10 = 20   2 x 9 = 18

Page 12

2x Facts

Go! Multiply to 2 x 10

2 ×6 = 12	2 ×5 = 10	2 ×4 = 8	2 ×10 = 20
2 ×1 = 2	2 ×0 = 0	2 ×2 = 4	2 ×4 = 8
2 ×8 = 16	2 ×7 = 14	2 ×5 = 10	2 ×3 = 6
2 ×3 = 6	2 ×2 = 4	2 ×6 = 12	2 ×7 = 14
2 ×10 = 20	2 ×8 = 16	2 ×9 = 18	2 ×8 = 16

Build a Mighty Memory Muscle!

After you finish this page, ask someone to read the questions aloud to you. Without looking, answer as many as you can from memory. For any you don't remember, find the answer, then repeat that multiplication sentence aloud. Memory experts say that repetition is a great way to strengthen your memory muscle and make remembering multiplication facts easy!

Page 13

3x Facts

Get Ready! Skip Count to Learn Multiples of 3
Shade the multiples of 3 on the chart.

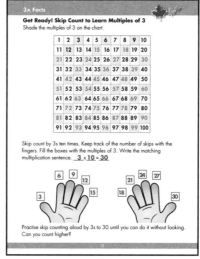

Skip count by 3s ten times. Keep track of the number of skips with the fingers. Fill the boxes with the multiples of 3. Write the matching multiplication sentence. 3 x 10 = 30

Practise skip counting aloud by 3s to 30 until you can do it without looking. Can you count higher?

Page 14

3x Facts

Get Set! Practise 3x Facts
Fill in the blanks to skip count from 3 to 30 and back again. Then complete the multiplication sentences.

3, 6, 9, 12, 15, 18, 21, 24, 27, 30
30, 27, 24, 21, 18, 15, 12, 9, 6, 3

3 x 0 = 0	3 x 4 = 12	3 x 8 = 24
3 x 1 = 3	3 x 5 = 15	3 x 9 = 27
3 x 2 = 6	3 x 6 = 18	3 x 10 = 30
3 x 3 = 9	3 x 7 = 21	

3 x 2 = 6	3 x 1 = 3
3 x 4 = 12	3 x 3 = 9
3 x 6 = 18	3 x 5 = 15
3 x 8 = 24	3 x 7 = 21
3 x 10 = 30	3 x 9 = 27

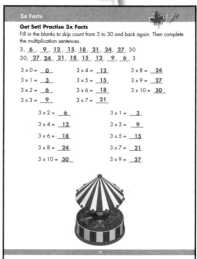

Page 15

3x Facts

Go! Multiply to 3 x 10

3 ×7 = 21	3 ×10 = 30	3 ×4 = 12	3 ×3 = 9
3 ×1 = 3	3 ×0 = 0	3 ×2 = 6	3 ×5 = 15
3 ×9 = 27	3 ×8 = 24	3 ×4 = 12	3 ×6 = 18
3 ×3 = 9	3 ×2 = 6	3 ×7 = 21	3 ×9 = 27
3 ×5 = 15	3 ×10 = 30	3 ×6 = 18	3 ×8 = 24

Build a Mighty Memory Muscle!

After you finish this page, ask someone to read the questions aloud to you. Without looking, answer as many as you can from memory. For any you don't remember, find the answer, then repeat that multiplication sentence aloud. Memory experts say that repetition is a great way to strengthen your memory muscle and make remembering multiplication facts easy!

Page 16

4x Facts

Get Ready! Skip Count to Learn Multiples of 4
Shade the multiples of 4 on the chart.

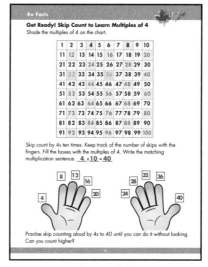

Skip count by 4s ten times. Keep track of the number of skips with the fingers. Fill the boxes with the multiples of 4. Write the matching multiplication sentence. 4 x 10 = 40

Practise skip counting aloud by 4s to 40 until you can do it without looking. Can you count higher?

Page 17

4x Facts

Get Set! Practise 4x Facts
Fill in the blanks to skip count from 4 to 40 and back again. Then complete the multiplication sentences.

4, 8, 12, 16, 20, 24, 28, 32, 36, 40
40, 36, 32, 28, 24, 20, 16, 12, 8, 4

4 x 0 = 0	4 x 4 = 16	4 x 8 = 32
4 x 1 = 4	4 x 5 = 20	4 x 9 = 36
4 x 2 = 8	4 x 6 = 24	4 x 10 = 40
4 x 3 = 12	4 x 7 = 28	

4 x 2 = 8	4 x 1 = 4
4 x 4 = 16	4 x 3 = 12
4 x 6 = 24	4 x 5 = 20
4 x 8 = 32	4 x 7 = 28
4 x 10 = 40	4 x 9 = 36

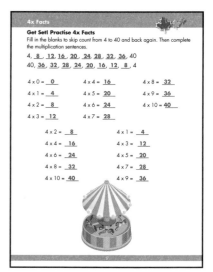

Page 18

4x Facts

Go! Multiply to 4 x 10

4 ×6 = 24	4 ×0 = 0	4 ×4 = 16	4 ×3 = 12
4 ×1 = 4	4 ×7 = 28	4 ×9 = 36	4 ×5 = 20
4 ×7 = 28	4 ×6 = 24	4 ×8 = 32	4 ×10 = 40
4 ×4 = 16	4 ×10 = 40	4 ×3 = 12	4 ×9 = 36
4 ×8 = 32	4 ×2 = 8	4 ×5 = 20	4 ×2 = 8

Build a Mighty Memory Muscle!

After you finish this page, ask someone to read the questions aloud to you. Without looking, answer as many as you can from memory. For any you don't remember, find the answer, then repeat that multiplication sentence aloud. Memory experts say that repetition is a great way to strengthen your memory muscle and make remembering multiplication facts easy!

Page 19

4x Facts

Learn the 4x Double-Double Trick
Here is a trick to multiply any number by 4. Just double the number that is to be multiplied by 4, and then double it again. (Remember: **Double** is another way to say **multiply by 2**.)

Example: 4 x 5 = ?

First, double the 5 to get 10.

Then, double the 10 to get 20.

So, 4 x 5 = 20

Try the **double-double** trick on the questions below.

4 ×6 = 24	4 ×10 = 40	4 ×3 = 12	4 ×2 = 8
4 ×4 = 16	4 ×7 = 28	4 ×9 = 36	4 ×8 = 32

Use the 4x double-double trick to check your answers on page 18.

Page 20

1x, 2x, 3x, 4x Facts Review

One More Lap! Review 1x, 2x, 3x, 4x Facts

2 x 2 = 4	4 x 9 = 36	1 x 7 = 7
4 x 6 = 24	3 x 8 = 24	3 x 3 = 9
3 x 7 = 21	4 x 10 = 40	2 x 8 = 16
2 x 10 = 20	2 x 7 = 14	2 x 6 = 12
1 x 5 = 5	3 x 6 = 18	4 x 7 = 28
4 x 3 = 12	4 x 2 = 8	3 x 4 = 12
3 x 5 = 15	2 x 3 = 6	1 x 10 = 10
4 x 4 = 16	2 x 5 = 10	2 x 9 = 18
3 x 9 = 27	3 x 2 = 6	4 x 8 = 32
2 x 4 = 8	4 x 5 = 20	3 x 10 = 30

Solutions

Page 21

5x Facts

Get Ready! Skip Count to Learn Multiples of 5
Shade the multiples of 5 on the chart.

1	2	3	4	5	6	7	8	9	10
11	12	13	14	15	16	17	18	19	20
21	22	23	24	25	26	27	28	29	30
31	32	33	34	35	36	37	38	39	40
41	42	43	44	45	46	47	48	49	50
51	52	53	54	55	56	57	58	59	60
61	62	63	64	65	66	67	68	69	70
71	72	73	74	75	76	77	78	79	80
81	82	83	84	85	86	87	88	89	90
91	92	93	94	95	96	97	98	99	100

Skip count by 5s ten times. Keep track of the number of skips with the fingers. Fill the boxes with the multiples of 5. Write the matching multiplication sentence. __5__ x __10__ = __50__

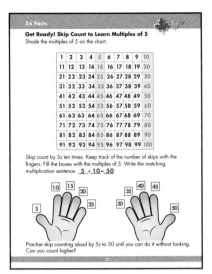

Practise skip counting aloud by 5s to 50 until you can do it without looking. Can you count higher?

Page 22

5x Facts

Get Set! Practise 5x Facts
Fill in the blanks to skip count from 5 to 50 and back again. Then complete the multiplication sentences.

5, __10__, __15__, __20__, __25__, __30__, __35__, __40__, __45__, 50
50, __45__, __40__, __35__, __30__, __25__, __20__, __15__, __10__, 5

5 x 0 = __0__   5 x 4 = __20__   5 x 8 = __40__
5 x 1 = __5__   5 x 5 = __25__   5 x 9 = __45__
5 x 2 = __10__   5 x 6 = __30__   5 x 10 = __50__
5 x 3 = __15__   5 x 7 = __35__

5 x 2 = __10__   5 x 1 = __5__
5 x 4 = __20__   5 x 3 = __15__
5 x 6 = __30__   5 x 5 = __25__
5 x 8 = __40__   5 x 7 = __35__
5 x 10 = __50__   5 x 9 = __45__

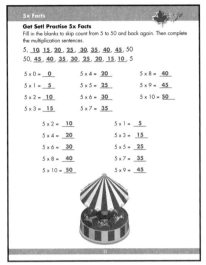

Page 23

5x Facts

Go! Multiply to 5 x 10

5 ×9 = 45	5 ×6 = 30	5 ×10 = 50	5 ×3 = 15
5 ×1 = 5	5 ×7 = 35	5 ×6 = 30	5 ×5 = 25
5 ×8 = 40	5 ×9 = 45	5 ×8 = 40	5 ×7 = 35
5 ×3 = 15	5 ×10 = 50	5 ×4 = 20	5 ×0 = 0
5 ×5 = 25	5 ×2 = 10	5 ×4 = 20	5 ×2 = 10

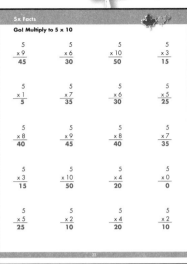

Page 24

6x Facts

Get Ready! Skip Count to Learn Multiples of 6
Shade the multiples of 6 on the chart.

1	2	3	4	5	6	7	8	9	10
11	12	13	14	15	16	17	18	19	20
21	22	23	24	25	26	27	28	29	30
31	32	33	34	35	36	37	38	39	40
41	42	43	44	45	46	47	48	49	50
51	52	53	54	55	56	57	58	59	60
61	62	63	64	65	66	67	68	69	70
71	72	73	74	75	76	77	78	79	80
81	82	83	84	85	86	87	88	89	90
91	92	93	94	95	96	97	98	99	100

Skip count by 6s ten times. Keep track of the number of skips with the fingers. Fill the boxes with the multiples of 6. Write the matching multiplication sentence. __6__ x __10__ = __60__

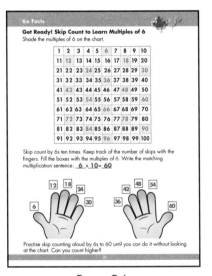

Practise skip counting aloud by 6s to 60 until you can do it without looking at the chart. Can you count higher?

Page 25

6x Facts

Get Set! Practise 6x Facts
Fill in the blanks to skip count from 6 to 60 and back again. Then complete the multiplication sentences.

6, __12__, __18__, __24__, __30__, __36__, __42__, __48__, __54__, 60
60, __54__, __48__, __42__, __36__, __30__, __24__, __18__, __12__, 6

6 x 0 = __0__   6 x 4 = __24__   6 x 8 = __48__
6 x 1 = __6__   6 x 5 = __30__   6 x 9 = __54__
6 x 2 = __12__   6 x 6 = __36__   6 x 10 = __60__
6 x 3 = __18__   6 x 7 = __42__

6 x 2 = __12__   6 x 1 = __6__
6 x 4 = __24__   6 x 3 = __18__
6 x 6 = __36__   6 x 5 = __30__
6 x 8 = __48__   6 x 7 = __42__
6 x 10 = __60__   6 x 9 = __54__

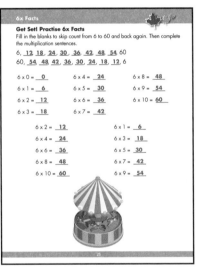

Page 26

6x Facts

Go! Multiply to 6 x 10

6 ×1 = 6	6 ×3 = 18	6 ×4 = 24	6 ×7 = 42
6 ×3 = 18	6 ×8 = 48	6 ×6 = 36	6 ×5 = 30
6 ×7 = 42	6 ×9 = 54	6 ×8 = 48	6 ×10 = 60
6 ×5 = 30	6 ×10 = 60	6 ×4 = 24	6 ×9 = 54
6 ×2 = 12	6 ×6 = 36	6 ×2 = 12	6 ×0 = 0

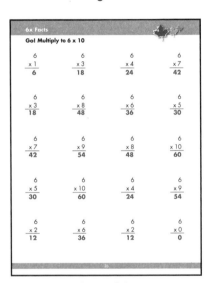

Page 27

7x Facts

Get Ready! Skip Count to Learn Multiples of 7
Shade the multiples of 7 on the chart.

1	2	3	4	5	6	7	8	9	10
11	12	13	14	15	16	17	18	19	20
21	22	23	24	25	26	27	28	29	30
31	32	33	34	35	36	37	38	39	40
41	42	43	44	45	46	47	48	49	50
51	52	53	54	55	56	57	58	59	60
61	62	63	64	65	66	67	68	69	70
71	72	73	74	75	76	77	78	79	80
81	82	83	84	85	86	87	88	89	90
91	92	93	94	95	96	97	98	99	100

Skip count by 7s ten times. Keep track of the number of skips with the fingers. Fill the boxes with the multiples of 7. Write the matching multiplication sentence. __7__ x __10__ = __70__

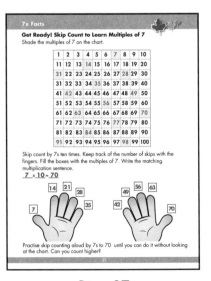

Practise skip counting aloud by 7s to 70 until you can do it without looking at the chart. Can you count higher?

Page 28

7x Facts

Get Set! Practise 7x Facts
Fill in the blanks to skip count from 7 to 70 and back again. Then complete the multiplication sentences.

7, __14__, __21__, __28__, __35__, __42__, __49__, __56__, __63__, 70
70, __63__, __56__, __49__, __42__, __35__, __28__, __21__, __14__, 7

7 x 0 = __0__   7 x 4 = __28__   7 x 8 = __56__
7 x 1 = __7__   7 x 5 = __35__   7 x 9 = __63__
7 x 2 = __14__   7 x 6 = __42__   7 x 10 = __70__
7 x 3 = __21__   7 x 7 = __49__

7 x 2 = __14__   7 x 1 = __7__
7 x 4 = __28__   7 x 3 = __21__
7 x 6 = __42__   7 x 5 = __35__
7 x 8 = __56__   7 x 7 = __49__
7 x 10 = __70__   7 x 9 = __63__

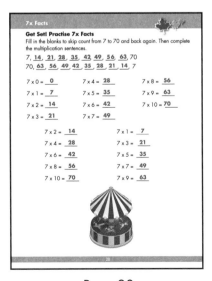

Page 29

7x Facts

Go! Multiply to 7 x 10

7 ×5 = 35	7 ×6 = 42	7 ×3 = 21	7 ×10 = 70
7 ×1 = 7	7 ×7 = 49	7 ×2 = 14	7 ×8 = 56
7 ×3 = 21	7 ×4 = 28	7 ×7 = 49	7 ×4 = 28
7 ×8 = 56	7 ×2 = 14	7 ×6 = 42	7 ×9 = 63
7 ×5 = 35	7 ×10 = 70	7 ×9 = 63	7 ×4 = 28

Page 30

5x, 6x, 7x Facts Review

One More Lap! Review 5x, 6x, 7x Facts

5 x 2 = 10	5 x 7 = 35	5 x 8 = 40
6 x 9 = 54	6 x 6 = 36	6 x 4 = 24
7 x 6 = 42	5 x 9 = 45	5 x 6 = 30
6 x 7 = 42	6 x 2 = 12	7 x 7 = 49
5 x 10 = 50	5 x 3 = 15	6 x 4 = 24
7 x 3 = 21	7 x 8 = 56	5 x 9 = 45
6 x 5 = 30	5 x 5 = 25	5 x 8 = 40
7 x 4 = 28	6 x 2 = 12	6 x 10 = 60
6 x 9 = 54	5 x 10 = 50	7 x 0 = 0
6 x 8 = 48	7 x 5 = 35	6 x 1 = 6
7 x 10 = 70	5 x 3 = 15	5 x 0 = 0

Page 31

1x, 2x, 3x, 4x, 5x, 6x, 7x Facts Review

Let's Go Around Again!
Review 1x, 2x, 3x, 4x, 5x, 6x, 7x Facts

2 x 2 = 4	7 x 7 = 49	3 x 6 = 18	3 x 3 = 9
5 x 2 = 10	3 x 9 = 27	7 x 3 = 21	2 x 8 = 16
4 x 6 = 24	6 x 9 = 54	2 x 9 = 18	2 x 6 = 12
5 x 3 = 15	7 x 6 = 42	7 x 4 = 28	1 x 1 = 1
3 x 7 = 21	7 x 9 = 63	4 x 2 = 8	7 x 7 = 49
5 x 6 = 30	2 x 4 = 8	5 x 9 = 45	4 x 7 = 28
2 x 10 = 20	5 x 5 = 25	2 x 3 = 6	3 x 4 = 12
4 x 3 = 12	4 x 9 = 36	6 x 2 = 12	5 x 8 = 40
5 x 4 = 20	6 x 4 = 24	6 x 8 = 48	2 x 9 = 18
3 x 5 = 15	3 x 8 = 24	2 x 5 = 10	1 x 3 = 3
1 x 10 = 10	4 x 10 = 40	5 x 10 = 50	6 x 10 = 60
6 x 6 = 36	6 x 5 = 30	3 x 2 = 6	4 x 8 = 32
5 x 3 = 15	2 x 7 = 14	7 x 10 = 70	7 x 5 = 35
7 x 4 = 28	5 x 8 = 40	4 x 5 = 20	3 x 10 = 30
4 x 4 = 16	2 x 3 = 6	7 x 3 = 21	6 x 2 = 12

Page 32

8x Facts

Get Ready! Skip Count to Learn Multiples of 8
Shade the multiples of 8 on the chart.

1	2	3	4	5	6	7	8	9	10
11	12	13	14	15	16	17	18	19	20
21	22	23	24	25	26	27	28	29	30
31	32	33	34	35	36	37	38	39	40
41	42	43	44	45	46	47	48	49	50
51	52	53	54	55	56	57	58	59	60
61	62	63	64	65	66	67	68	69	70
71	72	73	74	75	76	77	78	79	80
81	82	83	84	85	86	87	88	89	90
91	92	93	94	95	96	97	98	99	100

Skip count by 8s ten times. Keep track of the number of skips with the fingers. Fill the boxes with the multiples of 8. Write the matching multiplication sentence. 8 x 10 = 80

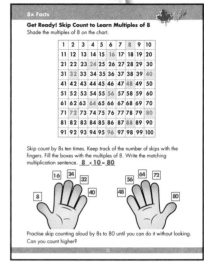

Practise skip counting aloud by 8s to 80 until you can do it without looking. Can you count higher?

Page 33

8x Facts

Get Set! Practise 8x Facts
Fill in the blanks to skip count from 8 to 80 and back to 8. Then complete the multiplication sentences.

8, 16, 24, 32, 40, 48, 56, 64, 72, 80
80, 72, 64, 56, 48, 40, 32, 24, 16, 8

8 x 0 = 0	8 x 4 = 32	8 x 8 = 64
8 x 1 = 8	8 x 5 = 40	8 x 9 = 72
8 x 2 = 16	8 x 6 = 48	8 x 10 = 80
8 x 3 = 24	8 x 7 = 56	

8 x 2 = 16	8 x 1 = 8
8 x 4 = 32	8 x 3 = 24
8 x 6 = 48	8 x 5 = 40
8 x 8 = 64	8 x 7 = 56
8 x 10 = 80	8 x 9 = 72

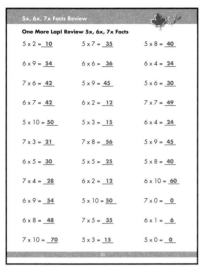

Page 34

8x Facts

Go! Multiply to 8 x 10

8 x 5 = 40	8 x 2 = 16	8 x 10 = 80	8 x 6 = 48
8 x 1 = 8	8 x 6 = 48	8 x 5 = 40	8 x 3 = 24
8 x 9 = 72	8 x 7 = 56	8 x 4 = 32	8 x 9 = 72
8 x 3 = 24	8 x 8 = 64	8 x 0 = 0	8 x 7 = 56
8 x 7 = 56	8 x 9 = 72	8 x 10 = 80	8 x 2 = 16

Page 35

9x Facts

Get Ready! Skip Count to Learn Multiples of 9
Shade the multiples of 9 on the chart.

1	2	3	4	5	6	7	8	9	10
11	12	13	14	15	16	17	18	19	20
21	22	23	24	25	26	27	28	29	30
31	32	33	34	35	36	37	38	39	40
41	42	43	44	45	46	47	48	49	50
51	52	53	54	55	56	57	58	59	60
61	62	63	64	65	66	67	68	69	70
71	72	73	74	75	76	77	78	79	80
81	82	83	84	85	86	87	88	89	90
91	92	93	94	95	96	97	98	99	100

Skip count by 9s ten times. Keep track of the number of skips with the fingers. Fill the boxes with the multiples of 9. Write the matching multiplication sentence. 9 x 10 = 90

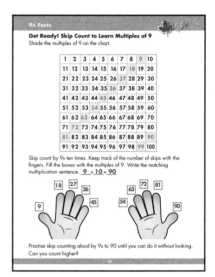

Practise skip counting aloud by 9s to 90 until you can do it without looking. Can you count higher?

Page 36

9x Facts

Get Set! Practise 9x Facts
Fill in the blanks to skip count from 9 to 90 and back to 9. Then complete the multiplication sentences.

9, 18, 27, 36, 45, 54, 63, 72, 81, 90
90, 81, 72, 63, 54, 45, 36, 27, 18, 9

9 x 0 = 0	9 x 4 = 36	9 x 8 = 72
9 x 1 = 9	9 x 5 = 45	9 x 9 = 81
9 x 2 = 18	9 x 6 = 54	9 x 10 = 90
9 x 3 = 27	9 x 7 = 63	

9 x 2 = 18	9 x 1 = 9
9 x 4 = 36	9 x 3 = 27
9 x 6 = 54	9 x 5 = 45
9 x 8 = 72	9 x 7 = 63
9 x 10 = 90	9 x 9 = 81

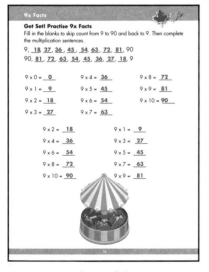

Page 37

9x Facts

Go! Multiply to 9 x 10

9 x 1 = 9	9 x 7 = 63	9 x 4 = 36	9 x 6 = 54
9 x 6 = 54	9 x 8 = 72	9 x 7 = 63	9 x 9 = 81
9 x 3 = 27	9 x 6 = 54	9 x 4 = 36	9 x 5 = 45
9 x 8 = 72	9 x 10 = 90	9 x 7 = 63	9 x 0 = 0
9 x 5 = 45	9 x 2 = 18	9 x 3 = 27	9 x 9 = 81

Page 39

9x Facts

Learn the Handy 9x Trick
Remember: Whatever number you want to multiply by 9, that's the finger you fold down.

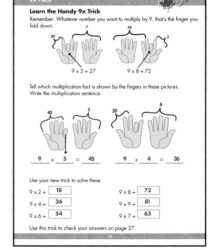

9 x 3 = 27   9 x 8 = 72

Tell which multiplication fact is shown by the fingers in these pictures. Write the multiplication sentence.

9 x 5 = 45   9 x 4 = 36

Use your new trick to solve these.

9 x 2 = 18	9 x 8 = 72
9 x 4 = 36	9 x 9 = 81
9 x 6 = 54	9 x 7 = 63

Use this trick to check your answers on page 37.

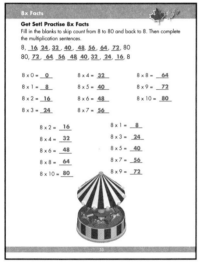
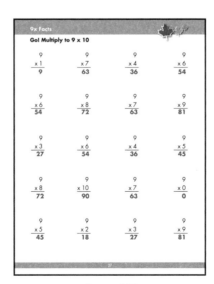
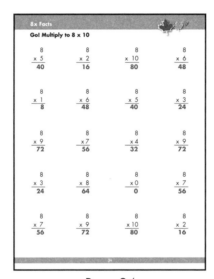

Page 40

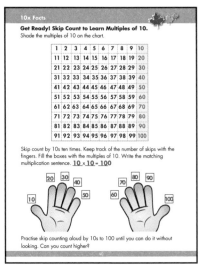

10x Facts

Get Ready! Skip Count to Learn Multiples of 10.
Shade the multiples of 10 on the chart.

1	2	3	4	5	6	7	8	9	10
11	12	13	14	15	16	17	18	19	20
21	22	23	24	25	26	27	28	29	30
31	32	33	34	35	36	37	38	39	40
41	42	43	44	45	46	47	48	49	50
51	52	53	54	55	56	57	58	59	60
61	62	63	64	65	66	67	68	69	70
71	72	73	74	75	76	77	78	79	80
81	82	83	84	85	86	87	88	89	90
91	92	93	94	95	96	97	98	99	100

Skip count by 10s ten times. Keep track of the number of skips with the fingers. Fill the boxes with the multiples of 10. Write the matching multiplication sentence. **10 × 10 = 100**

Fingers: 20, 30, 40, 50, 10 / 70, 80, 90, 60, 100

Practise skip counting aloud by 10s to 100 until you can do it without looking. Can you count higher?

Page 41

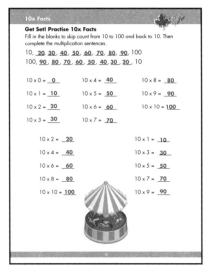

10x Facts

Get Set! Practise 10x Facts
Fill in the blanks to skip count from 10 to 100 and back to 10. Then complete the multiplication sentences.

10, __20__, __30__, __40__, __50__, __60__, __70__, __80__, __90__, 100
100, __90__, __80__, __70__, 60, __50__, __40__, __30__, __20__, 10

10 × 0 = __0__   10 × 4 = __40__   10 × 8 = __80__
10 × 1 = __10__   10 × 5 = __50__   10 × 9 = __90__
10 × 2 = __20__   10 × 6 = __60__   10 × 10 = __100__
10 × 3 = __30__   10 × 7 = __70__

10 × 2 = __20__   10 × 1 = __10__
10 × 4 = __40__   10 × 3 = __30__
10 × 6 = __60__   10 × 5 = __50__
10 × 8 = __80__   10 × 7 = __70__
10 × 10 = __100__ 10 × 9 = __90__

Page 42

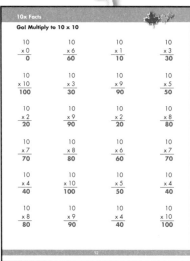

10x Facts

Go! Multiply to 10 × 10

10 ×0 = 0	10 ×6 = 60	10 ×1 = 10	10 ×3 = 30
10 ×10 = 100	10 ×3 = 30	10 ×9 = 90	10 ×5 = 50
10 ×2 = 20	10 ×9 = 90	10 ×2 = 20	10 ×8 = 80
10 ×7 = 70	10 ×8 = 80	10 ×6 = 60	10 ×7 = 70
10 ×4 = 40	10 ×10 = 100	10 ×5 = 50	10 ×4 = 40
10 ×8 = 80	10 ×9 = 90	10 ×4 = 40	10 ×10 = 100

Page 43

8x, 9x, 10x Facts Review

One More Lap! Review 8x, 9x, 10x Facts

8 × 2 = 16   9 × 8 = 72   9 × 3 = 27
10 × 6 = 60   10 × 10 = 100 8 × 8 = 64
9 × 7 = 63   8 × 3 = 24   8 × 6 = 48
8 × 10 = 80   8 × 7 = 56   10 × 7 = 70
10 × 3 = 30   9 × 6 = 54   9 × 4 = 36
9 × 5 = 45   8 × 2 = 16   8 × 9 = 72
10 × 4 = 40   10 × 2 = 20   10 × 8 = 80
9 × 9 = 81   8 × 3 = 24   9 × 10 = 90
8 × 4 = 32   8 × 5 = 40   8 × 1 = 8
10 × 9 = 90   9 × 2 = 18   10 × 5 = 50

Page 44

1x, 2x, 3x, 4x, 5x, 6x, 7x, 8x, 9x, 10x Facts Review

You're Off and Running! Review 1x, 2x, 3x, 4x, 5x, 6x, 7x, 8x, 9x, 10x Facts

9 × 10 = 90   3 × 7 = 21   3 × 5 = 15   4 × 4 = 16
1 × 2 = 2   9 × 3 = 27   8 × 7 = 56   9 × 7 = 63
10 × 8 = 80   5 × 6 = 30   7 × 1 = 7   7 × 7 = 49
5 × 2 = 10   10 × 5 = 50   10 × 10 = 100 8 × 2 = 16
8 × 9 = 72   2 × 10 = 20   9 × 8 = 72   3 × 9 = 27
9 × 4 = 36   9 × 2 = 18   6 × 6 = 36   6 × 9 = 54
10 × 7 = 70   8 × 5 = 40   8 × 4 = 32   7 × 6 = 42
4 × 6 = 24   4 × 3 = 12   5 × 3 = 15   7 × 9 = 63
8 × 6 = 48   8 × 5 = 40   9 × 9 = 81   2 × 4 = 8
5 × 3 = 15   5 × 4 = 20   7 × 4 = 28   6 × 6 = 36
8 × 8 = 64   9 × 6 = 54   9 × 5 = 45

Page 45

1x, 2x, 3x, 4x, 5x, 6x, 7x, 8x, 9x, 10x Facts Review

You're Off and Running! Review 1x, 2x, 3x, 4x, 5x, 6x, 7x, 8x, 9x, 10x Facts

5 ×5 = 25	7 ×3 = 21	3 ×2 = 6	2 ×9 = 18
4 ×9 = 36	7 ×4 = 28	7 ×10 = 70	6 ×10 = 60
6 ×4 = 24	4 ×2 = 8	4 ×5 = 20	4 ×8 = 32
3 ×8 = 24	5 ×9 = 45	3 ×3 = 9	7 ×5 = 35
4 ×10 = 40	2 ×3 = 6	2 ×8 = 16	3 ×10 = 30
6 ×5 = 30	6 ×2 = 12	2 ×6 = 12	6 ×2 = 12
2 ×7 = 14	6 ×8 = 48	4 ×7 = 28	7 ×3 = 21
5 ×8 = 40	2 ×5 = 10	3 ×4 = 12	1 ×6 = 6
3 ×6 = 18	5 ×10 = 50	5 ×8 = 40	10 ×10 = 100

Page 48

Multiplication Games and Puzzles

Find the Missing Numbers
Multiply the factor in the centre orange circle by each factor in the blue ring to get the product in the outer yellow ring. Fill in the missing factors and products.

Page 50

Multiplication Games and Puzzles

Multiplication Tic-Tac-Toe
Play like normal tic-tac-toe, but each player must correctly answer a multiplication fact before getting a square.

9×7 = 63	5×7 = 35	3×9 = 27		10×8 = 80	7×7 = 49	6×5 = 30
2×9 = 18	6×9 = 54	8×8 = 64		4×7 = 28	6×8 = 48	8×9 = 72
10×7 = 70	7×8 = 56	6×6 = 36		9×2 = 18	3×7 = 21	3×6 = 18
2×4 = 8	4×6 = 24	9×4 = 36		10×2 = 20	6×7 = 42	4×6 = 24
2×7 = 14	3×4 = 12	9×6 = 54		2×6 = 12	9×8 = 72	8×3 = 24
8×7 = 56	9×9 = 81	10×6 = 60		4×9 = 36	5×3 = 15	6×6 = 36
6×5 = 30	8×10 = 80	8×4 = 32		4×9 = 36	8×6 = 48	8×7 = 56
2×3 = 6	3×8 = 24	5×5 = 25		5×8 = 40	7×9 = 63	7×6 = 42
9×5 = 45	6×3 = 18	7×9 = 63		8×5 = 40	3×2 = 6	4×9 = 36

Page 51

Multiplication Games and Puzzles

Solve the Riddle
Solve the multiplication fact and print the letter in the box above the right answer.

5 × 5 = L	8 × 5 = Y	4 × 8 = P	4 × 9 = T
9 × 9 = I	3 × 5 = C	2 × 5 = S	2 × 6 = O
3 × 7 = A	6 × 7 = U	8 × 6 = H	3 × 3 = E
8 × 8 = N	4 × 5 = W	7 × 7 = M	8 × 3 = R

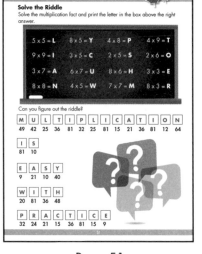

Can you figure out the riddle?

M U L T I P L I C A T I O N
49 32 36 81 32 25 81 72 15 21 36 81 12 64

I S
81 10

E A S Y
9 21 10 40

W I T H
20 81 36 8

P R A C T I C E
32 24 21 15 36 81 15 9

Multiplication Games and Puzzles

Missing Factors Fill Up
Fill in the missing factors in the boxes:

9 x 3 = 27	5 x 4 = 20	3 x 8 = 24	2 x 8 = 16
7 x 7 = 49	8 x 5 = 40	6 x 6 = 36	5 x 7 = 35
4 x 10 = 40	7 x 8 = 56	3 x 6 = 18	4 x 6 = 24
3 x 9 = 27	8 x 8 = 64	6 x 8 = 48	2 x 9 = 18
7 x 9 = 63	5 x 2 = 10	3 x 7 = 21	4 x 7 = 28
9 x 5 = 45	6 x 5 = 30	4 x 3 = 12	1 x 8 = 8

Page 52

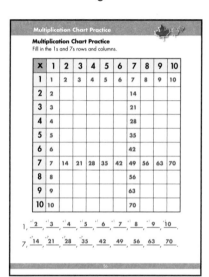

Multiplication Chart Practice

Multiplication Chart Practice
Multiply each factor in the left column by each factor in the top row. Fill in the missing products where the rows and columns meet.
Example: 2 x 2 = 4

x	1	2	3	4	5	6	7	8	9	10
1	1	2	3	4	5	6	7	8	9	10
2	2	4	6	8	10	12	14	16	18	20
3	3	6	9	12	15	18	21	24	27	30
4	4	8	12	16	20	24	28	32	36	40
5	5	10	15	20	25	30	35	40	45	50
6	6	12	18	24	30	36	42	48	54	60
7	7	14	21	28	35	42	49	56	63	70
8	8	16	24	32	40	48	56	64	72	80
9	9	18	27	36	45	54	63	72	81	90
10	10	20	30	40	50	60	70	80	90	100

Page 53

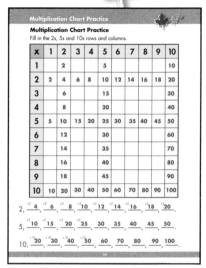

Multiplication Chart Practice

Multiplication Chart Practice
Fill in the 2s, 5s and 10s rows and columns.

x	1	2	3	4	5	6	7	8	9	10
1		2			5					10
2	2	4	6	8	10	12	14	16	18	20
3		6			15					30
4		8			20					40
5	5	10	15	20	25	30	35	40	45	50
6		12			30					60
7		14			35					70
8		16			40					80
9		18			45					90
10	10	20	30	40	50	60	70	80	90	100

2, 4, 6, 8, 10, 12, 14, 16, 18, 20
5, 10, 15, 20, 25, 30, 35, 40, 45, 50
10, 20, 30, 40, 50, 60, 70, 80, 90, 100

Page 54

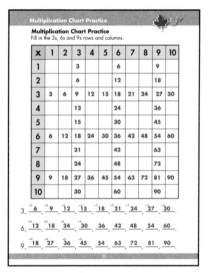

Multiplication Chart Practice

Multiplication Chart Practice
Fill in the 3s, 6s and 9s rows and columns.

x	1	2	3	4	5	6	7	8	9	10
1			3			6			9	
2			6			12			18	
3	3	6	9	12	15	18	21	24	27	30
4			12			24			36	
5			15			30			45	
6	6	12	18	24	30	36	42	48	54	60
7			21			42			63	
8			24			48			72	
9	9	18	27	36	45	54	63	72	81	90
10			30			60			90	

3, 6, 9, 12, 15, 18, 21, 24, 27, 30
6, 12, 18, 24, 30, 36, 42, 48, 54, 60
9, 18, 27, 36, 45, 54, 63, 72, 81, 90

Page 55

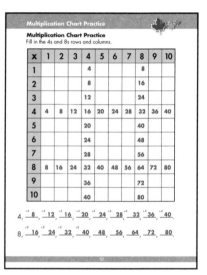

Multiplication Chart Practice

Multiplication Chart Practice
Fill in the 1s and 7s rows and columns.

x	1	2	3	4	5	6	7	8	9	10
1	1	2	3	4	5	6	7	8	9	10
2	2						14			
3	3						21			
4	4						28			
5	5						35			
6	6						42			
7	7	14	21	28	35	42	49	56	63	70
8	8						56			
9	9						63			
10	10						70			

1, 2, 3, 4, 5, 6, 7, 8, 9, 10
7, 14, 21, 28, 35, 42, 49, 56, 63, 70

Page 56

Multiplication Chart Practice

Multiplication Chart Practice
Fill in the 4s and 8s rows and columns.

x	1	2	3	4	5	6	7	8	9	10
1				4				8		
2				8				16		
3				12				24		
4	4	8	12	16	20	24	28	32	36	40
5				20				40		
6				24				48		
7				28				56		
8	8	16	24	32	40	48	56	64	72	80
9				36				72		
10				40				80		

4, 8, 12, 16, 20, 24, 28, 32, 36, 40
8, 16, 24, 32, 40, 48, 56, 64, 72, 80

Page 57